DAVID WINTER COTTAGES

First published in Great Britain in 1991
by John Hine Limited, 2 Hillside Road, Eggars Hill,
Aldershot, Hampshire GU11 3NB
This edition published in 1991
Copyright © John Hine Limited

Picture credits:
J S Library International, London. Pages 3 and 11
All-Sport Photo Ltd, London. Page 5 and 6 (photos by Pascal
Rondeau). 21 and 22 (photos by Russel Cheyne).
Colorific (Lucy Levenson), London. Page 7
Colorific (David Levenson), London. Pages 8, 9, 10 and 12

ISBN 1 871754 09 7 Knight's Castle & Ceremony of the Garter

Printed by Centurion Press Limited, London.

BRITISH TRADITIONS™

JUNE

KNIGHT'S CASTLE
&
CEREMONY OF THE GARTER

BY
JOHN HINE

Contents

INTRODUCTION

Grand Pomp and state ceremony, a strumpet and a philandering King, 14th century turmoil and plague, chivalry and chicanery are all in this the sixth volume of British Traditions. The naked facts about Medieval England are exposed and we see that life was not all pretty roses around the door and delicate flowers in the garden, for this England could be a frightening place to live in when one had the prospect of either a knife in the back, or death by pestilence, but astrology was there to cure you if you should be so foolish as to become ill.

GARTER DAY

I have been investigating the Most Noble Order of the Garter, which is all tied up with the business of chivalry. Edward the Third, who founded the Order in 1348, was influenced by Arthur and had reason to believe that King Arthur held Court, with his knights of the round table at Windsor; indeed, on a part of the site where Windsor castle stands today.

The concept of chivalry seems to have started with Arthur and would appear to have been at it's strongest when the country was in a state of vicious and violent civil strife. While peasants murdered for a stale loaf of bread, and barons with their troops plundered the weakest. England was in this condition in 1348 and getting worse by the hour. 1348 is also remembered for the Great Plague or Black Death, or Great Mortality, as it was referred to at the time. This was brought to England by black rats from the continent and after three epidemics, reduced the population from some four and a half million to about two million. This further loosened

the reigns of control and a total breakdown of law and order was narrowly avoided by the King, who had lost his own daughter, Joan, in the plague. We have no social history from the time of King Arthur, in fact, we have no substantIve evidence that he actually existed. Although, I have never doubted that he was more or less what folklore has told us he was.

Above: *At Windsor Castle, a guardsman protects the birthplace of chivalry*

Above: *Windsor provides the backdrop for the colourful procession*

Above: *The immaculate splendour of the Guards*

Edward the Third, was born in 1312. His father, Edward the Second, was a bit of a disaster as a King. He had an uncanny ability to upset the very people upon whom he relied to maintain the status quo. He always backed the wrong cause and made his life intolerable as a result. Finally, his wife Isabella, the daughter of King Philip the Fair of France, decided to take matters into her own hands. Without any difficulty, she put together an army supplied by dissident nobles, defeated her husband and forced him to abdicate and proclaim his son to be King. Edward the Second's troubles did not come to an end with this - he was murdered two years later.

The tradition of Garter Day today is part ceremonial, part religious, part practical and part parade. The most televised element is the

Above: *The traditional costume of the Yeoman of the Guard*

Above: *Her Majesty Queen Elizabeth the Second*

procession which is shown around the world because it is so colourful and so "English". The original celebrations were held during the month of April on the eve of St George's Day. However in the month known for "April showers bring May flowers", more parades were cancelled due to the heavy rain, than actually happened. Now it is held in June, which is a bit more reliable. Recently, the day chosen has been the Monday of Royal Ascot week.

Above: *Heralds, Knights and Royalty*

Most of the Garter Day ceremony happens behind closed doors and the likes of us can only imagine the scenes.

Firstly, the investiture of new Knights is carried out in a private ceremony in the throne room of Windsor castle. The Sovereign places a garter on the left leg, below the knee, of the new Knight and a blue ribbon over the left shoulder. The Dean of Windsor then presents the Knight with a bible and asks him to swear an oath that he will obey the statutes of the Order and the laws of the realm. Next comes lunch, which is a grand affair held in the Waterloo room, after which the Knight Companions, the Officers of the Order, and the Officers of the Arms, assemble in St George's Hall, to await the arrival of the Sovereign. In due course, the procession sets off to St George's Chapel along a route lined by splendidly uniformed members of The Lifeguards, The Blues and Royals, part of the Household Brigade, and soldiers from the Grenadier

Guards in their scarlet jackets and bear skins, or busbies. A military band plays rousing music to encourage the knights to put their best foot forward.

This is the order of the 1988 parade:-

The Constable and Governor of Windsor Castle

The Governor of the Military Knights of Windsor

The Military Knights

The Officers of Arms

The Heralds;

Fitzalen Pursuivant Extraordinary and Rouge Croix Pursuivant

Blue Mantle Pursuivant and Portcullis Pursuivant

Rouge Dragon Pursuivant and Beaumont Herald Extraordinary

Wales Herald Extraordinary and Somerset Herald

Lancaster Herald and Richmond Herald

Windsor Herald and York Herald

Norroy and Ulster King of Arms followed by

21 Knights of the Garter

His Royal Highness The Duke of Kent

Her Majesty Queen Elizabeth the Queen Mother and

His Royal Highness The Prince of Wales

Page of Honour

Black Rod and The Secretary

The Register and Garter

The Chancellor and The Prelate

The Sovereign

accompanied by

His Royal Highness The Prince Philip, Duke of Edinburgh

Pages of Honour

The Silver Stick in Waiting and the Field Office in Brigade

in Waiting and their Adjutants

The Clerk of the Cheque and Adjutant, and The Lieutenant

A Detachment of The Queen's Body Guard of the Yeomen

of the Guard

The Ensign

Her Majesty's Body Guard of the Honourable Corps of

Gentlemen at Arms will be on duty in the Chapel

After the parade then follows the Church service, which starts with the National Anthem and is followed by the Lord's Prayer, Te Deum Laudamis, Creed. Lesson, Anthem and Prayers. The hymn ," Now thank we all our God", is sung before the benediction of the order and the Blessing. The Queen and her Knights return to the Upper Ward of Windsor Castle in a carriage procession (except when it is raining, in which case they all go by car.) By the time they get back, I am sure all they want to do is get out of those heavy costumes and connect with a nice cup of tea.

The Garter Day tradition is spectacular for the pomp and ceremony that can be found nowhere else in the world. The British undoubtedly have a talent for such grand occasions, and I am thinking particularly of the marriage of Prince Charles to Lady Diana. The organisation was incredible, a sight I will never forget, and the whole thing went without even a hint of a hitch. The military men who organise these spectaculars, say it is all down to planning, but that must be only part of the story. The Garter Day parade is a mini Coronation, but we do not get to see too many of those, I am very happy to say. The other two occasions on which the boat is put out every year are the The Trooping Of The Colour and The State Opening Of Parliament, both of which are very worth watching and were considered for our series of British Traditions. We chose Garter Day because of the ancient connections with chivalry and medieval England.

KNIGHT'S CASTLE

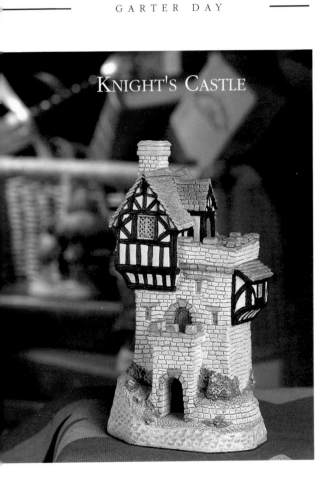

By now, I hope you will have got a feeling of what living in 14th century England might have been like. People clustered into communities, to give themselves mutual protection against bands of marauding footpads and cut-throats who would kill for a loaf of bread. More of a threat were the errant gangs of heavily armed plunderers, who scoured the country looting and pillaging and generally making a nuisance of themselves. Sometimes these ruffians were mounted and could take on a detachment of soldiers, so they posed a very great threat. Worse still were the disloyal Barons who owed no allegiance to the Monarch and had no intention of behaving like servile vassals cringing before their liege. They could besiege a small castle or attack a town and make off with their spoils before the local garrison could get troops to quell their meddling. Simple Simon, minding his own business and going innocently about his affairs, was threatened on all sides and only felt secure when he was in a crowd of other Simple Simons. But not

everybody could live in the villages and towns. Somebody had to cultivate the land and protect sheep, cattle and pigs while they grazed, wherever there was fresh grass for them to eat. This could be a chancy business and the wretched fellows given this work must have felt very vulnerable. The squire or Knight who owned the land would make life as secure as possible by building fortified dwellings into which his herdsmen could retreat

when word had it that the bad guys were in the area. Attached to these mini fortresses, or sometimes inside them, would be stockades to hold the precious animals, which were often what the miscreants wanted to steal.

David Winter thought long and hard about Garter Day and the period when the Order Of the Garter was founded. He wanted his piece to be a place in which a Knight of the Garter might have lived and at the same time represent the concept of it having to be fortified. Knight's Castle is certainly a place in which one could feel safe, and even if it was attacked, the feeling is that the outcome would be satisfactory. There is only one door on the ground level, and it would be made of the stoutest oak and be at least four inches thick. Behind it would be steel bars set into the stone -work on either side of the arch, so that even if a battering ram was used it would still not give way. The upper door would be as strong but the inhabitants could get onto the balcony and tip boiling oil onto the attacking rogues. This would also be where archers could let off a salvo of arrows and make the invaders wish they had stayed in bed. The higher balcony would be put to the same use and Knight's Castle could give a good account of itself if threatened.

The small window slits were for more archers to shoot from a well protected position and would also

be used to push away ladders, when they were used. I very much like the Knight's living quarters perched on top. For the majority of the time, the Knight could enjoy the view and take his morning jug of herb infusion on the balcony. David has brought the two ideas of house and fortress together to make an interesting piece that obviously has seen many adventures over the centuries.

The accommodation inside the main tower would be chillingly frugal. People would only be in it at times of danger and they would be there to fight, so furniture and beds would be unnecessary. The kitchen would dish up survival food but nothing else. The stone stairway would run round the main walls leading to the various levels and archers lobbies. Weapons would be kept in steel lockers and issued only when necessary; the Knight would be giving himself a potential extra problem if he allowed his serfs to be armed all the time, for who knows, they might turn and use them on him, perish the thought. David's Knight of the Order Of the Garter would be secure and comfortable in this castle.

THE QUEST FOR POWER

In the year 1345, King Edward the Third was thirty five years old. He was married to Phillippa, daughter of Count William of Hainault. At a feast to celebrate the recapture of the French Port of Calais, the King's mistress, the Countess of Salisbury, let her garter drop to the floor. This provoked much sniggering and jocularity amongst the courtiers, but the King rebuked the assembly and picked up the garter and put it on his own leg and said " Honi Soit Qui Mal Y Pense " (Shame on him who thinks evil of it) and announced that the Garter would soon become an emblem of great significance.

There is some historical evidence to suggest that this may have happened. Everything else that follows is fiction.

The questions that flash into my mind are:

 1. *Why did the King have a mistress ?*

 2. *Why was the fact that he had a mistress known publicly ?*

EDWARDVS REX

Edward the Third

3. Why did the Countess of Salisbury allow her garter to drop to the floor?

4. Why was the Garter about to become an item of significance?

It seemed to me that these questions should be answered, so here we go. Obviously, the character of the Countess of Salisbury is central to everything that happened in the middle of the fourteenth

Edward picked up the garter

The Countess of Salisbury was central to everything

century. The stories that would have made the headlines at the time were; The Black Death, The Peasant's Revolt, and The Hundred Years War. The Black Death or Great Mortality as it was known at the time, decimated the population and it attacked peer and serf without distinction. Archbishops, dukes and earls were struck down alongside butchers, bakers and candlestick makers. The plague was classless, and not even the monarch was safe from it's inevitable shroud for he lost his daughter Joan to the plague.

The Peasant's Revolt was brought about by the poor reaching the point at which they had nothing to lose through rebellion. They went on an orgy of vengeance against the classes that were better off; in the certain knowledge that whatever happened to them, it could not be worse than the sufferings of their everyday lives. The Hundred Years War was a bit of a farce because both sides spent lives and money on it, as if they were going out of fashion.

Mediaeval headlines

In the end, both sides were in exactly the same position as one hundred years earlier.

But, to get back to the four questions

One: The king had a mistress because all kings had mistresses, it was the fashion, since Kings very rarely married for love. Marriages were political alliances in a time when blood lineage was of supreme importance. As Edward had married the

33

Wealth and social advancement could follow if the King took a shi

o one's wife

daughter of the ruler of Hainault, in what is now called Belgium, he had no need to conquer it as his son would be King of England and Hainault. The Queen was treated with exemplary respect and given her due position at all official functions, but she would not be expected to be intimate with the King, other than for producing true blood heirs. The King sought female company from within his court and the quickest way for a nobleman to advance his position and wealth, would be for the Monarch to take a shine to his wife. Kings were always very generous in these matters.

Two: The whole thing was public because there was no disgrace, it was the accepted custom. I am afraid to say that what was good for the gander was not good for the goose, as the Queen knew; if she were to risk the blood purity of the line, she would be in deep trouble.

Three: the Countess let her garter drop as a signal to her followers - all will be revealed, and

Four: Why did the garter become an item of significance - why indeed ? There had to be a reason and I have attempted to dig it out from the under layers of thick historical dust. I have arrived at a theory which demonstrates the wholesale wickedness of the times and the lengths to which evil people will go to attain power.

Matilda, the cunning Countess

Matilda, Countess Of Salisbury was one of history's most cunning women. She was in the class of Catherine the Great of Russia, and Queen Savronola of Madagascar, the less said about these ladies the better. Matilda had been made to marry the Earl Of Salisbury when she was only sixteen. The earl was then forty three years old and both his two previous wives had died giving birth - the commonest form of death for women in the 14th century. She had led a

Matilda had been made to marry at sixteen

boring life in the country, which she hated as she found rural pursuits loathsome and repulsive. She was not a rustic and yearned for life at Court in London or Windsor. She spent most of her time on her hair, make up and having gowns made, in the knowledge that she had been blessed with as many endowments as any young woman could wish for. All she wanted was the opportunity of putting them to some practical use. Matilda's dull and devout husband spent his time managing his estates and praying. Matilda never prayed, she had more than enough confidence in herself and had no need for any divinity to assist her.

Whenever she wanted the Earl to do something or give her another dressmaker, she had only to flirt a little and he became putty in her hot palms. He, in return got his way with establishing his line with three strong, healthy sons. Matilda had given him what he wanted, now she was out to get what she desired. She decided that three sons was

He became putty in her hands

enough and persuaded the Earl that she had done her duty as a wife, and was it not now time to go to London and live at court. She tempted the Earl with the lure of the additional fortunes he could make and the other titles he might have bestowed upon him, if he found favour with the King.

What she meant, of course, was if SHE found favour with the KIng, but she did not go into that !

The Salisburys moved to London

So, the Earl and Countess of Salisbury, together with their household, moved to London where Matilda found something she had never dreamed about, streets upon streets of dressmakers. She visited them all, with Alice her long suffering maid, in order to be able to find the one who could design and make dresses that would do justice to the flawless body they would adorn. Eventually, she chose her preferred dressmakers and set them to work making gowns fit for the most dazzling and stunning Venus that had ever been seen at the court of King Edward the Third.

Matilda next called upon many of the grand ladies in town, ostensibly to introduce herself, but in reality to learn everything she could about the King. She subtly brought all topics of female conversation round to the only subject that interested her, and soon she had a mental dossier about him. She learnt that he was a devout and sincere man who was nobody's fool. She learnt he was deeply influenced by King Arthur and his codes of chivalry. He had ambitions to recreate the round table at Windsor and invest Knights with the highest ideals. Next, she discovered that he was preoccupied with regaining the English territories in France and was already waging a successful war. As far as she was able to ascertain, he had only two vices. The first was an ambivalent attitude towards the black arts and the second was the fact, well known to all at

Matilda called on many grand ladies

King Arthur was a great influence on Edward

court, that he had a passion for beautiful women. Matilda was delighted and now set about the difficult task of assembling the forces she would need if she was going to be as successful as she knew she could be. She sent Alice to seekout the magicians and sorcerers who would lead her to the pagan priests, whose help she was going to need.

Witchcraft and devil cults had existed for thousands of years and were still strong in the 14th century. This is no surprise, as the only defence doctors had against the plague was astrology ! It is a well known fact that when a new religion is established in any country, the god or gods of the old religion become the devil of the new. However the old one still had a very large following, particularly in rural areas. It was not until the 18th century that it became uncommon - 1,200 years after the introduction of Christianity.

Alice had little difficulty in making the right contacts and was soon able to introduce her mistress to the Pagan High Priest. The Countess learnt from him that many of his followers were in high places throughout the land. Indeed , several were at court and a few were very close to the King. She discussed parts of her plan with him. He only had to know enough and certainly not everything she had in her contorted mind.

The Countess was introduced to the Pagan High Priest

She had always known that she was destined for greatness

The air of London and the feeling of being at the centre of the universe, had brought her true personality to the fore. She wanted everything she saw, but more than anything else, she wanted power. She had always known that she was destined for greatness. Why else had she been given such physical and mental attributes, if they were not intended to be used, she asked ? She passionately believed her future was to be the greatest person of her time and resolved to waste no precious moments in bringing that about. But her entire plan hung on the King's reaction when he met her. She had little doubt what it would be, but it needed testing. The great banquet that was to be held the next day would be the right opportunity.

She had the chosen dress in her wardrobe, she had bought the sheerest gossamer seven denier stockings, her hair was perfect and she knew she looked good; so goeth for it, she thought to herself. Alice had spent the whole day preparing the

Countess for the presentation at court and had to admit to herself that the end product was "not bad". Matilda and the earl made the short journey to court in an uncomfortable horse drawn carriage. It reverberated every cobble in the roadway through to the seat and she was thankful that she did not have to remain radiant for more than a few minutes. They arrived at court along with every other nobleman and spouse in the land, or so it seemed.

Matilda's confidence was still intact even though the competition was plentiful. Every other grand lady in the land was dressed to kill and intent on stealing the limelight. She surveyed the competition and had to admit that the coming contest would not be the walkover she had hoped it would be. She crossed her fingers, made the sign of thirteen and entered the great hall with her head held high and her mind on conquest. She held the arm of the Earl,

Windsor Castle, scene of the banquet

*St George, the slayer of dragons, symbol of chivalry to
English noblemen*

her husband, but she was as unaware of him as if he were a cardboard cut - out, since she had no place for him in her grand scheme. St. George himself could not have distracted Matilda from the target of her affections. A fanfare sounded, the door to the royal apartments opened and the royal procession made it's way into the Great Hall.

The king's duty was to receive each courtier in turn , find the right words to say that would consolidate his position, as head of State, and ensure the loyalty of the nobleman, who would supply the armies he needed for his war against the French. The Earl of Salisbury could supply a regiment or two, so it was seemly that he should spend several moments in conversation with him. Although his speech was appropriately political, his senses were unable to disguise the fact that he was aware of the presence of a wholly exceptional lady at his court. He was confused, he did not want to show his reaction too quickly, for fear that the lady would take advantage. Yet he knew he could not let her leave without being aware of the impression she had made on him. Matilda's second sense told her of his dilemma, and she adroitly positioned herself away from the assembly, so that he could speak to her without anybody overhearing them. The king did exactly what she had planned him to do and came across to her and engaged her in convivial conversation. From every word that was said, and every posture he took, she knew that her aims and objectives were attainable and that her plan was now flawless. She knew she could at last implement her diabolical scheme, now that she knew the King's desires were within her control.

The banquet was a great success. The King had made discreet eye contact whenever he had the chance and Matilda had bashfully responded on every occasion, having not taken her eyes off him all evening. Later that night, in the privacy of her own chamber, she put quill to parchment and wrote a

A letter bearing the King's heavy wax seal

thank you letter that said all the right and proper things, but left so much between the lines that the King would have no doubt as to her true feelings. She dragged Alice out of bed and made her run to the palace with the letter, and she told her to stay there until she had a reply to bring back. A day later, Alice reappeared, bearing a letter with the King's heavy wax seal. Ripping it open, Matilda was overjoyed to read that the King was anxious to meet

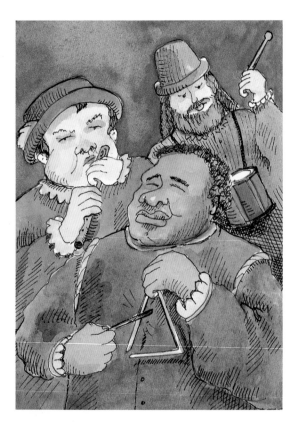

Count Basie and ye minstrels

her in private and summoned her to be at his garden pavilion at noon the next day. The letter also contained details of the route she should take to avoid being seen by gossip columnists who would have a field day if they spotted her.

So it came about that Matilda achieved her ambition to become the most important person in the land through the power she could exert as the King's mistress. At a great feast, organised as a celebration of her being acknowledged in her new rank, the court was at its most lavish. The best gold plate was laid out and the Count Basie Band had been hired for the dancing. As was the custom, the King led Matilda onto the floor for the first quadrille and everybody stood back to watch and admired the handsome sovereign and his spectacular mistress. The King was demonstrably distraught and whispered something in Matilda's ear. They stopped dancing, the band stopped playing and the Countess elegantly stooped as if in a curtsy. As she rose, she

stepped to one side to reveal her garter on the floor. The dumbstruck court could not believe their eyes and there was much sniggering and jocularity, but the King rebuked the assembly and picked up the garter, put it on his own leg and said " Honi Soit Qui Mal Y Pense " and announced that the Garter would soon become an emblem of great significance. This showed how quick witted King Edward the Third was, and how able he was to

think fast, for the cause of his discomfort had been the knowledge that his legging had come adrift and he was about to expose a great deal of royal flesh. He did indeed make the Garter significant by founding The Most Noble Order of the Garter the very next day. He gave it the motto of " Honi Soit Qui Mal Y Pense ."

Honey save me bally pants

ABOUT DAVID WINTER

David does a great deal of his work in his delightful little cottage in Ireland, beside which are three out buildings that used to be a one man pottery, but nowadays are used as studios and guest accommodation. His mother and father, Faith and Freddie, often go there for their holiday. Faith uses one of the studios for preparing the next large scale sculpture she is about to undertake and for making maqettes, or miniature models, of the main piece. The cottage and sheds were built along the bank of a broad stream which babbles it's way past, making those hypnotic sounds of water rushing over pebbles. There is a sward of grass between the buildings and the stream, which leads onto a paddock with a camp at the end of it, where the children have bonfires and incinerate their suppers. There is not another house in view and the road bridge, that crosses the stream by the entrance, has little traffic with only an occasional tractor and trailer passing by. It is a haven of serenity and of silken stillness, a restful refuge and an ideal setting for an artist to be receptive to inspiration.

There is an amazing square tower on open land behind David's cottage, which overlooks the bridge and stream. Evidently, square towers by bridges are a common sight in Ireland, and they must have something to do with being watch towers where guards would look for threatening mobs of irregulars. When these were spotted, bracken would be burnt on the top of the stone tower to raise the alarm, and, if possible, a rider dispatched to the town with information about the raiders. Today, contented cows graze around the tower totally undisturbed by bands of vagabonds. David estimates that the tower must be 80 ft high and other intrepid fellows like Jonno Stuart and Tim Moore, have often climbed the treacherous spiral staircase all the way to the top to enjoy the view and throw things at yours truly sitting on the grass refusing to go up to even the first floor. Heights are not for me as the yellow streak down my back testifies.

AND FINALLY.....

This has turned out to be one of the more action packed Traditions, which is not what I had expected when setting out to explore Garter Day and everything associated with it. I was intrigued to find the Earl of Salisbury during my researchers, for he is arch spy-master of the Guy Fawkes saga, Robert Cecil, who was given this title some two hundred and forty years later. This means that the Earldom died out through lack of sons and was available to be given out out again at a later date. Just as well, because I am sure they would have sued for all the wicked things I said about Matilda, Countess of Salisbury.